TOUGH DECISIONS

50 Activities in Values & Character Ed~

Ann Bourman

J. WESTON
WALCH
PUBLISHER
PORTLAND, MAINE

1   2   3   4   5   6   7   8   9   10

ISBN 0-8251-2870-6

Copyright © 1990, 1997
J. Weston Walch, Publisher
P.O. Box 658 • Portland, Maine 04104-0658
Printed in the United States of America

Contents

III. At Home

IV. Among Friends

To the Teacher

This book is designed for teachers who wish to provide their students with learning activities in character education—also called "proper" behavior, morals, values, ethics, or other terms that apply to the specific goals of teachers and students. As they do the lessons, which involve reading, discussion, writing, and role-playing skills, students deal with such values as compassion, tolerance, honesty, courtesy, and obedience to the law. The lessons include problems that arise in the community, in the school, at home, and among friends.

These lessons are designed for middle school and junior high school students, grades six to nine—the grades that I teach. Because lessons in character education work best if they deal with real-life situations in which young people may actually find themselves, I have taken virtually every situation in these fifty activities from the experiences of my students. They have told me about them, I have seen the incidents happen, or I have heard students repeat them to friends. By doing activities involving experiences of young people their own age, your students will learn to tackle similar problems of their own.

Following are suggestions for five ways to use these lessons. If you think of other ways that would suit your students better, use them!

1. The lessons can be used as a basis for student writing. If you choose this option, have each student select a lesson or assign a lesson to him or her. Tell students to read the description of the problem and to ask you any questions they have about the situation described. Then have students write answers to the questions under **Thoughts and Questions.** To make this a useful language-skills exercise, as well as one in character education, tell students to avoid using sentence fragments as they answer the questions. Show them how to answer a question in a complete sentence without repeating all the words in the question. For example, to answer the question "What would you do if you were Rose?" students might write "If I were Rose, I might . . . ."

Variations: As an alternative to assigning a lesson to each student in the class, you could treat the activity set as a learning center to be used by different students at different times. Another approach would be to assign lessons to individual students who have completed other class work. They could do the activities for enrichment purposes or extra credit.

2. The lessons can be used in cooperative learning groups. If you choose this approach, begin by giving either a pair or group of three students one activity sheet. Instruct them to read the problem together and then discuss and debate how they would answer the questions. One group member should record the answers. Have the group give the written answers to you.

How are cooperative learning groups formed? Sometimes teachers form the groups so that they will include a very bright student, a slow student, and average students. Brighter students should help the slower students, and all group members should contribute to the work. At other times teachers allow students to form their own groups, choosing other students with whom they are comfortable. I recommend both methods. In either case, however, you should not hesitate to move a student from one group to another to correct disruptive behavior or to place a student where he or she will work more effectively.

Often the only problem a group has is getting started. I frequently find that several groups are well into their work the first time I check on them, while others are wondering how to begin. Offer help to those slow-starting groups, especially if you are just beginning to use cooperative learning. Help them avoid arguing for a prolonged period over which alternatives to select and how to begin. Suggest ways to get started.

3. A third way to use the lessons is a variation on number 2. Instead of having students give their written answers to you, tell them to lead a class discussion of the problem their group has discussed and written about. One student might read the problem on the activity sheet to the class. The other student(s) might then read the questions, together with the answers the group has written. Group members encourage other class members to suggest alternative answers.

4. A fourth way the activity sheets can be used is as a basis for role-playing activities for groups of three or four students. (Most of the lessons provide roles for four characters.) If you choose this approach, have group members read the description of the problem and then discuss the questions. Each student in the group then assumes the role of one of the characters listed under **Characters for Role-playing.** Using their discussion of the questions as a resource, students again discuss solutions to the problem, this time speaking from the point of view of the character they are role-playing. Decide whether you will grade the group based on their role-playing performance or whether you will also require a written summary of what the group determined through its role-playing.

5. A fifth variation expands on number 4. After group members have practiced discussing the problem from the point of view of their various characters, one student from the group reads the problem to the class. Group members explain the problem thoroughly to the class and then name the character roles they have assumed. Based on their previous "rehearsal," group

members then present a role-playing production to the class in which they discuss the problem. Decide on the length of each presentation depending on the size of your class, the abilities of your students, and the time you want to spend on the assignment. A written summary would probably not be required for this oral presentation.

I prefer to use choices 3, 4, or 5 in my own classroom because it is not difficult to get middle school and junior high school students to discuss issues like those presented on these activity sheets. If you can get the students to scream vociferously over these issues, you have engaged them in critical thinking and character education. This is the kind of arguing you want them to do. It is the critical thinking that will help them develop the values and ethics that are the subjects of these lessons.

—Ann Bourman

Should Maria Reveal That She Has Witnessed an Automobile Accident?

On her way to school one morning, Maria saw an accident involving two cars. Luckily, it was not a very serious one, and no one was hurt. Maria had seen one driver pull out from the curb without looking or signaling. He hit the side of a passing car and scraped it badly.

The drivers of the two cars got out and argued about who was at fault. As far as Maria could see, she was the only witness to the accident. Should she walk up to the driver who did not seem to be at fault—the passing car— and offer to be a witness for her against the man who pulled out from the curb without looking? Or should she walk away unnoticed, and not "get involved"?

Maria can't decide!

Thoughts and Questions

1. Should Maria offer to be a witness or not?

2. No one was injured in the accident. Does that make it less important for Maria to speak up than if there had been injuries?

3. Have you ever seen an accident happen, as Maria did? What action, if any, did you take?

4. What values will Maria show she feels are important if she steps forward as a witness?

Characters for Role-playing

1. Maria

2. the driver of the passing car

3. the driver of the car that pulled out from the curb

4. a man or woman who stepped out of a house near the accident after hearing the crash

5. a police officer or judge in court dealing with the accident

Should
Ted Report
the Shoplifter?

When Ted walks into his local supermarket to buy a few items he needs, he spots a man who is evidently shoplifting. The man is slipping a few packages of cheese and luncheon meat into his coat pocket and inching toward the exit. He is very old and unkempt and looks very poor. Judging by his appearance, he may even be a "street person." He probably needs the food very badly.

On the other hand, it is wrong to steal.

Ted can't decide what to do, and he has to think fast. It seems wrong not to report the man to the store manager, but if the man is caught, he may suffer consequences out of proportion to his crime. Ted also knows that there are few places that homeless men and women can get help. He knows that the store or eventually a court might get help for the man.

Ted is confused!

Thoughts and Questions

1. Should Ted report the man or not?

2. It is wrong to steal. Does it make any difference that the man doing the stealing is very poor and needs what he is taking?

3. Have you ever seen a situation similar to this one? What action, if any, did you take?

4. What values are in conflict here?

Characters for Role-playing

1. Ted
2. the old man
3. the store manager
4. a security guard or police officer

Should Wayne Admit
He Witnessed
the Shooting?

It was Saturday night and Wayne was returning home from his school's football game. He sat on the front stoop to wind down from his excitement over throwing two touchdown passes. In the dark Wayne heard voices two houses away. He recognized the voices of his friends, Juan and Dave.

"You promised to pay me for the *delivery*, Dave shouted angrily. Juan handed him money. "Hey, wait a minute, you owe me more," retorted Dave.

Two gunshots rang out. Wayne watched as one person fell to the ground. He ran into the house and called 911, but he refused to identify himself to the dispatcher.

The next day Wayne read an account of the incident in the paper. It asked that anyone with information about the shooting contact detectives at 555-1345. Wayne was scared. He wasn't sure what to do.

Thoughts and Questions

1. What values do Juan and Dave show they lack by doing drugs? What values do they need to learn?

2. What values will Wayne show he feels are important if he contacts the detectives about the incident? How might Wayne's action or inaction affect the future of the neighborhood?

3. Have you ever been in a situation similar to Wayne's or do you know someone who has? What action, if any, did you take?

4. How can drug abuse affect your life—now and in the future?

Characters for Role-playing

1. Wayne
2. Juan and Dave
3. the dispatcher
4. an EMT
5. two detectives

Tough Decisions

Should Diane Lie About Her Age to Get into a Movie?

Diane and some friends decide to go see a movie one weekend afternoon. In their town, anyone over the age of twelve must pay adult prices to enter a movie theater. As if that weren't annoying enough, some movie theaters do not admit viewers under the age of thirteen, even at the adult price. They claim the movies contain material not suitable for younger children.

Diane decides to use her fifteen-year-old sister's I.D. card to gain admittance to a film she wants to see. It is for people over the age of thirteen and she is twelve. No one will look closely at the I.D. photo, and she and her sister look a great deal alike. She feels the film is very suitable for a person her age, and she has to pay the adult price. She feels that her use of her sister's I.D. card is therefore not really dishonest.

Thoughts and Questions

1. What values is a society trying to promote when it reserves certain films for people of certain ages? Does it make much difference, considering what is always available for viewing on television?

2. Do you think Diane is being dishonest?

3. Would her action be all right if her parents approved of her seeing the movie?

4. Have you or your friends ever lied at a movie theater to see a film you were not supposed to see, or pretended to be a younger age so you could pay less?

Characters for Role-playing

1. Diane

2. Diane's sister Charlotte

3. Diane's mother

4. the ticket seller at the movie theater

Should
Scott Call
the Police?

On the way home from school one afternoon, Scott sees a man lying in the street near the curb. Scott notices that he is the same old drunk he's seen stumbling down the street or collapsed on the sidewalk many times. What a fool he is, Scott thinks.

The man makes Scott especially angry because he reminds him of his own father, who drank himself to death.

Scott wants to walk by and ignore the man, but something tells him the man may be in very serious trouble this time. He knows he should call the police. The man might be attacked by other "street people." He might be very ill. He might even be dead!

What should Scott do?

Thoughts and Questions

1. What important values will Scott be showing if he calls the police?

2. Should Scott try to help the man on his own?

3. Have you ever seen a person in the street like this? What did you do? What *would* you do if you saw someone like this?

4. What would you want a stranger to do if the person in the street were a friend or relative of yours?

Characters for Role-playing

1. Scott

2. a woman or man in a nearby house from which Scott makes a call to the police

3. a police officer

4. an EMT

Should Clara and Her Classmates Support the Death Penalty?

Clara's class has become involved in a discussion of arguments for and against the death penalty as a punishment for murder. Different students voice their opinions. Disturbed by the discussion, Clara suddenly bursts out:

"Not one of you knows what you're talking about. I do. I never knew my father because he was killed in a bar when I was only two years old. He was no drunk—he just stopped by a bar for one drink on his way home from work one night. Some guy he had never seen before picked a fight with him. My father tried to shove past him to leave, but the man pulled a gun out and shot him. He died right there. The man was tried and convicted, but he only served three years in jail. How can that be? I don't know if I favor the death penalty or not, but my father's life was worth more than three years!"

The class is stunned; the discussion continues.

Thoughts and Questions

1. What values does a society show if it has the death penalty for murder?

2. What values does a society show if it does not have the death penalty, and its harshest punishment is life in jail?

3. Do you favor the death penalty? Do you disapprove of it? Explain your position. Is it used in your state?

4. How does it happen that a number of murderers in our society serve such short sentences? How could this be corrected?

5. What do you think you might have said to Clara after she told her story to the class?

Characters for Role-playing

1. Clara

2. Lucy, a girl in the class who favors the death penalty

3. Ron, a boy in the class who is against the death penalty

4. the teacher of the class

Should Ricardo Report the Shoplifter Who Is His Good Friend?

Ricardo and Nelson decided to go shopping together one afternoon. At the local mall they wandered through a hobby shop, several clothing stores, and a sporting goods store. Then they went into a restaurant and had some hamburgers.

When they were finished eating, they went into a stereo store. Ricardo was shocked when he noticed that Nelson was shoving some small packages of blank cassette tapes into his jacket pockets. "Hey!" Ricardo whispered. "What are you doing? You're stealing! You could get caught and be in big trouble!"

"It's nothing," Nelson whispered back. "I've done it before and I didn't get caught. Besides, this is a rich store. They can afford it."

Ricardo is stuck. He does not want to report his best friend. On the other hand, he does not want his best friend to be arrested for theft. What should he do?

Thoughts and Questions

1. Should Ricardo report his friend in the store? What values will he be showing if he does that? Is there any way he can just get his friend to put the tapes back where he got them?

2. Does it make any difference that the store is rich and can afford it? Who really pays for shoplifting?

3. What can Ricardo say to Nelson later, when they have left the store?

4. Friends try not to report their friends for poor behavior (see number 1 at left). What values are friends trying to uphold in such cases?

Characters for Role-playing

1. Ricardo
2. Nelson
3. a guard in the store who sees what Nelson is doing
4. the manager of the store
5. one of Nelson's parents

How Can Jenny
Get Nicer Clothes
for School?

Jenny is poor and wears worn-out clothes to school. Some students make fun of her. She feels so hurt by their remarks that she often stays home from school to avoid them.

One morning a teacher quietly takes her aside and asks her why she is absent from school so often. The teacher thinks she knows what the problem is. She is friendly and kind to Jenny. Jenny finally has a chance to tell someone the problem that has been bothering her. Perhaps there is a way to get help. On the other hand, she does not want to embarrass her family.

Should she tell the teacher the truth about her absences and her shabby clothes? Or should she make up some sort of excuse?

Thoughts and Questions

1. Is it right for the teacher to ask Jenny about something she suspects is a family problem? What value is the teacher showing if she does that?

2. Should Jenny try to solve her problem all by herself? If she does, what value will she be demonstrating? Or will she just be stubborn?

3. Should people always try to solve problems all by themselves?

4. Should people sometimes try to solve problems with help from others? When? What values are shown when you help your friends with their problems?

5. Find out what services your own school has that might help a student like Jenny.

Characters for Role-playing

1. Jenny
2. the teacher who questions Jenny
3. one of Jenny's friends
4. one of the students who makes fun of Jenny
5. one of Jenny's parents

How Can Rico Get Other Students to Stop Making Fun of His Spanish Accent?

Rico is sick of having students make fun of his Spanish accent. Having come from Nicaragua, he has been in the United States for just one year. He is proud of the progress he has made learning to speak, read, and write English. His family is proud of him, too, and they rely on him as a translator.

But some boys at school make fun of the way he pronounces certain words. They imitate him and laugh at him. They also threaten to beat him up if he tells any school officials what they have been doing.

Should Rico ask a teacher or another adult in the school for help? He wants to handle the situation himself, but it has been going on for a long time.

Thoughts and Questions

1. When some people hear a foreign accent, they think the speaker is ignorant or not very smart. Is this what a foreign accent tells you about a person?

2. What values are lacking in the students who make fun of Rico?

3. What values would students be demonstrating if they got to know Rico and helped him with his English?

4. Do you know any people with foreign accents? Which countries are they from? How are they treated in regard to their language ability?

5. Have you ever tried to learn a language other than the first language you spoke? Was it easy? Was it difficult?

Characters for Role-playing

1. Rico
2. a boy who makes fun of his English
3. a boy who defends Rico
4. a teacher who overhears the problem

How Can Sam Avoid Being Robbed of Money at School?

At school Sam is often stopped by older boys who demand that he give them money. They threaten to beat him up if he does not hand over the money. They find him in the bathroom, cafeteria, or gym, where it is often difficult for a teacher to see what is happening.

So far, Sam has been giving them small amounts of money to protect himself, but he knows he can't let it go on forever. But how can he stop it?

Thoughts and Questions

1. What ethics and values do the boys lack when they rob Sam? Is there any way Sam can protect himself without going to a teacher? Is there anything he can say to get the boys to leave him alone?

2. Should Sam go to a teacher? Isn't it the job of the teachers to protect the students?

3. How much of this type of behavior have you seen at your school? Have you ever been a victim? How do you think the problem should be handled?

4. What are all the ideas you can come up with that will stop such dishonest and frightening behavior at your school, or any school?

Characters for Role-playing

1. Sam

2. Omar, Sam's friend

3. Nicholas, a boy who has taken money from Sam

4. a teacher who sees Nicholas try to take money from Sam

Should Sherrie Stay at School to Take a Test, Even Though She Feels Ill?

Sherrie tells her friend Carol that she feels ill and thinks she has a fever. Carol feels Sherrie's forehead and it really feels hot! She tells Sherrie to go to the nurse's office to be checked. Then she can telephone her mother so that she can go home.

Sherrie doesn't want to go to the nurse. She says it would make her miss an important math test in the afternoon, and the poor grade she has in the class now might drop even further. Carol tries to tell Sherrie that it's good to want to do her school work, but if she's ill she won't do well anyway. The teacher will probably let her make it up later.

Should Sherrie go to the nurse or push herself to go to class and take the test?

Thoughts and Questions

1. Should Sherrie go to the nurse or not?

2. Should Carol tell a teacher or the nurse if Sherrie won't?

3. What value is Sherrie trying to uphold under difficult circumstances?

4. What value will Carol be demonstrating if she "goes against" her friend and tells the nurse or the teacher?

5. Did you ever stay in school to finish your work even though you did not feel well? What was it like? How did it work out?

Characters for Role-playing

1. Sherrie

2. Carol

3. the school nurse

4. a teacher, perhaps Sherrie's math teacher

5. Sherrie's mother

Should Michael Report the Classmate Who Cheats on the History Tests?

Michael is sick of seeing one of his classmates cheat on nearly every history test. Marian hides notes or looks on someone else's paper every time there is a test. It's hard to see how she has gotten away with it, as the teacher watches carefully. Michael knows that many students cheat once in a while, and he has done it a few times himself, but it makes him mad to see this girl do it constantly.

After one particular test, the teacher praises Marian for having the highest score in the class. Michael and several others who had seen her cheat again vow that they will tell the teacher.

Thoughts and Questions

1. What values does Marian need to learn to avoid cheating on tests?

2. What pressures and influences seem to you to make students cheat on tests and other school work?

3. How do you feel or react when you see students cheating? Do you tell the teacher about it? Should Michael tell the teacher?

4. Tell the truth: Have you ever cheated on a test in class? What made you do it? Did it help you do well on the test? Were you caught?

Characters for Role-playing

1. Michael

2. Marian

3. Ana, another student who has seen Marian cheating

4. the teacher of the class

What Should Kenny Do About the Class That Is Rude to the Substitute Teacher?

When Kenny walked into his science class one day, he was upset that a substitute teacher who had been there several times before was about to begin the class. The class had been told to be especially polite to subs, but this woman had herself been very rude to many students for no reason at all!

During the first part of the class, the students worked well, but several times students asked the substitute reasonable questions, and she replied rudely. Then the trouble began. Some boys threw papers. Some students got up and wandered around the room. One girl called the teacher a nasty name when the teacher's back was turned, and she could not see who did it. The assistant principal of the school walked into the room and all the noise stopped. He demanded to know what was going on.

Thoughts and Questions

1. What does the substitute teacher need to learn about handling a class properly and being polite?

2. What does the class need to learn about how to act when a substitute is present?

3. Why do you think it is that classes tend to "act up" when another teacher takes the regular teacher's place?

4. Kenny wants to have a discussion with the assistant principal about this particular substitute and tell him what this woman does. Should he? What should he say?

Characters for Role-playing

1. Kenny
2. Nedra, a girl in the class
3. the assistant principal
4. the substitute teacher

What Can Jackie Do
About the History Teacher
Who Took Her Math Paper?

Jackie's history teacher caught her doing math homework during history class and took her paper. Jackie is an all "A" student in history and had finished all of her history work. She was just using time left at the end of the period to get other work done. She was not disruptive. Why did the history teacher get so upset? If her history grades were poor, the teacher's reaction might make sense.

After class, the teacher tells Jackie that she is rude and inattentive and does not want to return Jackie's math paper to her. Jackie explains that her history work was all done, so she was using the rest of the period wisely for work instead of playing around, as so many other students do. Should the history teacher give back the math paper?

Thoughts and Questions

1. What values is the teacher trying to teach Jackie?

2. What values is Jackie showing she has developed on her own?

3. What do you think the teacher should do with Jackie's math paper? Would your answer be any different if Jackie had poor grades in history?

4. What have you seen teachers in your school do when a student is doing work from another class, rather than the work of the class he or she is in at the moment?

Characters for Role-playing

1. Jackie

2. Jackie's history teacher

3. Jackie's math teacher

Should Daniel Reveal That He Speaks Japanese?

When Daniel's homeroom teacher asks if anyone in the class speaks any language other than English, he cannot decide how to reply. Daniel speaks Japanese at home with his immigrant parents.

The teacher is asking the question so that the counseling office can have a list of students who might be able to help non-English-speaking students who enter the school. Daniel would be glad to help, but has already experienced anti-Japanese and anti-Asian name-calling and mean comments, and does not wish to call further attention to his background. Offering help might cause more prejudice. He can't decide whether to volunteer his knowledge.

Thoughts and Questions

1. Should Daniel raise his hand and reveal his ability to speak Japanese?

2. Should Daniel go up to the teacher privately and allow him/her to add his name to the list?

3. What should Daniel do when he does face prejudiced remarks against himself in school?

4. What values will Daniel be exhibiting if he puts his name on the list?

5. What values do students need to learn when they criticize Daniel's nationality and race?

Characters for Role-playing

1. Daniel
2. Daniel's homeroom teacher
3. Daniel's counselor
4. a new Japanese-speaking student who needs Daniel's help
5. a student who has made prejudiced remarks about Daniel

Should Peter
Reveal Who Stole
the Yearbook?

During the last week of school when the yearbooks are distributed, a monitor from each class is asked to return the books of those who are absent that day to the school office.

That afternoon it is discovered that Peter's class is one short of the number of books that should have been returned. Peter knows that Kelly, the girl who took the books to the office, stole one. She plans to give it to Joel, a boy she likes very much. Peter heard Kelly tell a friend what she had done. Joel thinks Kelly has purchased the book for him.

Peter wonders if he should report the theft. The school will probably find out who did it anyway, once they check the records carefully and see that Kelly was the last person to handle the missing book. Peter wonders how serious a punishment Kelly will receive, and if she'll lose Joel's friendship.

What should Peter do?

Thoughts and Questions

1. What value does Kelly lack in this situation?

2. Should Peter report what he has heard, even if he's sure the school will find out who took the book without his help?

3. What might Joel do if he accepts the book and then finds out Kelly stole it?

4. What would be a fair punishment for Kelly?

Characters for Role-playing

1. Peter

2. Kelly

3. Joel

4. a school official who is told about or discovers the theft

Is Mr. Harris

Abusing

His Students?

Rumors have been going around the school that Mr. Harris, a popular English teacher, has been seen touching girls' bodies in places he should not touch them. Linda once saw him lean over and touch her friend Kristy's leg, but she wondered if it was an accident, as he was also picking up a piece of paper from the floor near Kristy.

Then one day, as Linda was walking up the stairs to a class, she saw Mr. Harris ahead of her, and she clearly saw him pinch a girl on her buttocks! Linda was shocked and did not know what to do. She had read articles about sexual abuse, and her mother had taught her to refuse to be touched where she did not want to be touched. But is this that serious? If Linda reports this to the principal, will she be believed? If so, will a popular teacher be fired? It was so confusing!

Thoughts and Questions

1. Sexual abuse can damage a person for life, so isn't it important that Linda report what she has seen?

2. It will be sad if Mr. Harris repeats his behavior and is fired, but what important value will the school be upholding if this happens?

3. Do you personally know anyone who has experienced sexual abuse? Did he or she get proper help?

4. You are in charge of telling Linda exactly what to do and how to go about it. Tell her!

Characters for Role-playing

1. Linda
2. Kristy
3. the girl Mr. Harris pinched
4. Mr. Harris
5. the principal of the school

How Can Felicia

Convince Her Teacher

That the Drawing Is Hers?

Felicia is famous for not doing her homework. But she *did* do the drawing that her art teacher, Ms. Beckett, had asked for. Felicia put her paper on her desk before the tardy bell rang and walked over to talk with a friend. When she returned to her desk the paper was gone!

She told Ms. Beckett she had brought the assignment to class, but now it was missing. The teacher helped her look for it but it did not turn up.

The next day, Felicia's work was posted on the bulletin board with Sylvia's name on it! Sylvia had obviously cut Felicia's name off the paper and added her own. Felicia ran to tell Ms. Beckett, but the teacher did not know how to react. Felicia rarely did her work, and Sylvia always did hers. Since it had been a homework assignment, Ms. Beckett had not seen the work as it was being done. Luckily, Damien, a boy in the class, had gone to Felicia's house so they could work on their drawings together. He was willing to tell Ms. Beckett who had done the work. Would she believe him?

Thoughts and Questions

1. What values is Sylvia lacking when she puts her name on another person's work?

2. How have you seen teachers react to students who rarely do their homework? Have their reactions been helpful? How would you suggest teachers help such students?

3. How can Felicia and Damien convince Ms. Beckett that the work on display is Felicia's?

4. Ms. Beckett did not know how to react. This shows that she did not automatically accuse Felicia of not doing her work, even though she had so often neglected it in the past. What does this show you about Ms. Beckett and her values?

Characters for Role-playing

1. Felicia
2. Sylvia
3. Ms. Beckett
4. Damien

Tough Decisions

How Can the Class
Get Jeremy to Do
His Own Work?

Jeremy asks to copy classwork and homework from everyone, all the time! He never does his own work because he spends all his time playing sports. It's a miracle he passes tests on his own! His classmates know that lots of students do the very same things from time to time, but Jeremy is too much! They've all had enough of his pestering. They decide to tell him to change his habits and do his own work for a change.

What should the other students say to Jeremy?

What should the other students do if Jeremy won't quit his constant pestering and copying?

Thoughts and Questions

1. What values does Jeremy need to learn?

2. Why might he learn the values he needs from his friends when his parents and teachers have already been unable to teach him those values?

3. Do you know a student like Jeremy? How do you handle him or her?

4. Should the students get a teacher or counselor they admire to help them with Jeremy?

Characters for Role-playing

1. Jeremy

2. Nadine, a girl who is tired of Jeremy's bad habits

3. Alfred, a boy who does not really care what Jeremy does

4. a friendly teacher or counselor who would like to help Jeremy and the students he annoys

How Can the Students Be Convinced to Be Courteous to Maika?

At the school talent show, the performers do their usual acts—singing popular songs, performing the latest dances, and doing comedy acts. Maika, a talented musician, performs a Mozart sonata on the piano. Some students in the audience laugh and talk; others try to quiet them down so that Maika can be heard. Some students clap at a pause in hopes that she'll stop playing.

When the piece is over, Maika bows and leaves the stage gracefully, but she is near tears. She knew her performance would not be as popular as the latest rock music, but she was proud of her skills and her friends had encouraged her to perform.

Should the student who is announcing all the acts say anything to the audience? Will that help the situation or just increase Maika's embarrassment?

Thoughts and Questions

1. What values is Maika showing by being able to develop great skill at the piano and by being able to perform in front of an audience?

2. What values do the rude members of the audience need to learn?

3. Have you ever performed in any sort of school talent show? If so, how did it feel to be up there in front of all those people?

4. What should Maika's friends say to her after the performance?

Characters for Role-playing

1. Maika

2. Maika's mother, a member of the audience and a professional musician

3. Eduardo, the student Master of Ceremonies for the show

4. Lisa, Maika's good friend

Should Eddie

Report the

Hackers?

Sam and Eva spent every free period working in the computer room. One afternoon, Eddie was in the computer room finishing his history report. Sam and Eva were whispering and giggling about something.

"Hey, what's so funny?" Eddie asked.

"We're *shopping*!" quipped Sam.

Eddie picked up his disk and left, not quite understanding Sam's comment.

A few days later, Eddie noticed Eva wearing a brand new outfit complete with expensive western boots. Sam was carrying around a new lap-top computer and a cellular phone.

At lunch, Eddie overheard Sam tell Eva to meet him in the computer room. He said he had enough new credit card numbers to charge up a storm.

That's *it*, thought Eddie. They've gotten into some office computer and stolen credit card numbers. They're headed for big trouble. What should I do?

Thoughts and Questions

1. Computers are available in most schools. What rules or guidelines, if any, should there be for using school computers?

2. What values are Sam and Eva lacking? What is the "big trouble" they may be heading for?

3. Some kids think computer hacking is no big deal. What kind of crime is computer hacking? How would you feel if your privacy were invaded?

4. What would you do if you were Eddie? Why?

Characters for Role-playing

1. Eddie
2. Sam
3. Eva
4. the computer resource teacher

How Can the Other Students Help Alex in Sports?

Alex is the boy the other students pick last to be on a sports team. He has little skill in any sport. When he tries to make a basket or run with a football or hit a baseball, he always messes up. If the teacher didn't insist he take part, he'd always be on the bench.

Alex knows that he will never be a star in sports, but he does the best he can. Luckily, though he's often picked last for a team, the other students are not cruel to him. When he does hit the ball or make the basket, they cheer him on! What else could they do to encourage him to do his best in sports?

Thoughts and Questions

1. What values does Alex show by trying so hard to do well at something where he will never be a star?

2. What values do the students show by cheering him on?

3. Some parents criticize and scream at their own children when they see them perform poorly at a sports event. Why would they do this? What must it do to their children?

4. How have you seen students treated at your school when they are not doing well at sports? Is better treatment needed?

Characters for Role-playing

1. Alex

2. Brian, a friend who tries to encourage him to join the basketball team

3. Mr. Boston, the basketball coach

4. Alex's father

Is Fatima
Wearing
a Hat?

Fatima is the only Moslem girl in her school. Her family moved to the United States from the Middle East and they observe all the customs of their religion. Fatima wears a scarflike head-covering that her religion requires. Most students scarcely notice it; a few make ill-mannered comments about it, which Fatima ignores. She is popular and has even been elected to the student council.

One day, Bill, a boy in one of her classes, says, "How come she gets to wear that scarf when there is a school rule that says the rest of us can't wear hats in the building?" Not too many of the students respond to Bill's comment; they think it is a silly interruption. But Bill repeats his question, and the students discuss it.

Thoughts and Questions

1. What important values is Fatima trying to uphold?

2. What values does the school demonstrate by allowing her to wear an item that she must wear to honor her religion?

3. Do you know of any religious rules that would not be honored in public schools? (For example, some religions allow only prayer for healing injuries or curing illnesses. They do not allow their followers to get help from doctors or to use any medications or have any vaccinations. Nevertheless, those students would not be allowed into a public school without proof of required vaccinations. Why?)

4. Are you allowed to wear hats in your school? Why or why not? If they are not permitted, what are the reasons?

Characters for Role-playing

1. Fatima

2. Bill

3. a student who defends Fatima's right to wear her head-covering

4. the teacher of the class

Does Rachel Have
to Dissect
the Animals?

Rachel refuses to dissect animals in her science class. This is not because she can't stand the sight of blood. She thinks animals should not be used in experiments. She admits a few animals may be needed in some medical experiments to test vaccines or medicines, but she has read sickening articles about how animals are used in painful experiments to test cosmetic products. Some animals have even been shot so doctors can practice repairing gunshot wounds in people!

Rachel thinks dissection in her school classroom is an immoral waste of animal life and will not participate. She can even quote recent court cases that defend her point of view.

Should the teacher make Rachel participate? Should she receive a low grade if she will not do what is required of all the other students?

Thoughts and Questions

1. What good values does Rachel show when she refuses to dissect animals?

2. What could the teacher do instead of making Rachel participate or giving her a low grade?

3. What is your opinion about using animals in experiments? Under what circumstances do you approve of it? Under what circumstances do you disapprove of it?

4. Did you know that courts in the United States have made decisions about students with Rachel's attitude? Try to find out what those courts have decided. Perhaps your history teacher or the librarian can help you.

Characters for Role-playing

1. Rachel
2. Rachel's science teacher
3. the principal of the school
4. one of Rachel's parents

Does Mrs. Floyd
Have to Remove the
Christmas Tree Display?

Mrs. Floyd, the principal of the school, has a lovely Christmas tree and holiday decorations displayed in the main office of the school during December. Everyone enjoys the pretty ornaments, the sparkling lights, and the scene of the birth of Jesus.

In history class Ricky brings up the question of the separation of church and state. The class has studied the Bill of Rights, and Ricky wonders if such a display is proper in a public school.

Ricky says, "I belong to a church, and I love that display in the office. We have one like it at home and a big one at my church. But this is a public school. Not everyone here is a Christian. Some people belong to other religions and some have no religion at all. Does that display really belong there?"

Thoughts and Questions

1. What values is Mrs. Floyd demonstrating with her lovely decorations?

2. What values is Ricky demonstrating by bringing up his questions?

3. What is your opinion of the use of Christmas decorations in a public school? You need to read and understand Amendment I in the Bill of Rights if you do not already know it. Your teacher can help you.

4. Do you have Christmas decorations in your school each year? Have you ever heard anyone questioning their use?

Characters for Role-playing

1. Ricky

2. Deirdre, a girl who feels the display in the school is fine

3. Mrs. Floyd

4. the teacher of the history class

How Should
Gary Wear
His Hair?

Everyone at school was talking about Gary's unique hairstyle. He had a barber cut his hair short on the top and on the sides and shape a skull and crossbones into what little hair remained. A curlicue, which he had dyed green, hung from the back of his head. He got plenty of stares and comments. Finally, he shoved a boy who criticized his hair, and a minor scuffle ensued. Both boys were suspended for one day for the fight.

A school official later told Gary that since the school had no rules about how students were to wear their hair, he could continue to come to school with any hairstyle he pleased. He was advised, however, that his unusual appearance would probably invite future comments, stares, and criticism, and that if he got in a fight again, he would be punished again.

Thoughts and Questions

1. Should Gary continue to wear his hair in his unusual style?

2. When a person dares to be different, what risks does he or she take?

3. What are some standards for deciding when it is important to appear or act or think in a manner that is different from the people around you? When is it foolish or silly or not worth the consequences to do so?

4. What value is Gary trying to maintain? Is there any other way he could maintain that same value?

Characters for Role-playing

1. Gary
2. the student who had a fight with Gary
3. a school official advising Gary
4. a student who supports Gary
5. one of Gary's parents

Should Mrs. Edwards

Accept

the Gifts?

When Michelle's family left for a two-week trip to France during the school year, Michelle asked her favorite teacher, Mrs. Edwards, what she would like as a souvenir. Mrs. Edwards replied, "I'd like to see a journal of your trip. I'll accept it in place of the classwork you'll miss. Also, bring me a delicious chocolate bar!" They laughed together, and agreed to the deal.

When Michelle returned, she brought the journal and the chocolate, but she also brought Mrs. Edwards a very expensive bottle of perfume and a gorgeous silk scarf! Mrs. Edwards knew that Michelle's father was a wealthy businessman and could easily afford the gifts, but she felt uncomfortable. In addition, an informal school rule asked teachers not to accept expensive gifts from students. What should Mrs. Edwards do?

Thoughts and Questions

1. What values will Mrs. Edwards show if she simply accepts the gifts and thanks Michelle?

2. Is there any way Mrs. Edwards can explain that the gifts are too expensive for her to accept without hurting Michelle's feelings?

3. Why might a school have a rule telling teachers not to accept expensive gifts from students?

4. Give Mrs. Edwards advice as to what she should do in this case.

Characters for Role-playing

1. Michelle
2. Mrs. Edwards
3. Michelle's father
4. the principal of the school

How Should
the Judge
Punish the Vandals?

"How could Mr. Jones flunk me in math?" moaned Joe, as he and his friend Patty walked toward Joe's house. "I'll show him."

Joe was angry. He ran into his basement and came out holding a can of spray paint. Patty followed Joe back to school. By then it was dark. Joe began spraying graffiti on the wall beneath Mr. Jones' classroom. He encouraged Patty to do the same. Reluctantly she did.

Suddenly the two vandals were blinded by the lights of a police cruiser. The officer stepped out of the car and assessed the damage.

"He told me to do it," cried Patty. "I didn't really want to."

The officer drove them both home. On the way, he made it clear to Joe and Patty that they were being arrested on charges of vandalism.

Thoughts and Questions

1. What value is the police officer trying to teach Joe and Patty?

2. Why isn't "He told me to do it" a good excuse? Would it influence a judge?

3. What type of punishment would you suggest if you were the judge?

4. Do you see much graffiti around your school or your neighborhood? Who does it and why? How does it make the school or the neighborhood look to you and to people from other communities? What can be done about graffiti?

Characters for Role-playing

1. Joe and Patty
2. the police officer
3. Joe's parents
4. Patty's parents
5. the judge

Should Andrew

Dress Differently

for Class?

Mrs. Brody called Andrew up after class one day to talk to him about the clothes he was wearing. He had on dirty blue jeans that were covered with paint stains. He had on a T-shirt that had a picture of young women with almost no clothes on. Mrs. Brody told Andrew that his clothes were not proper for school and that she did not want to have him come to her class again dressed in that manner.

Andrew argued politely that the T-shirt was one he had purchased at a concert, and that it was the same picture that was on a record album made by his favorite rock group. He also said that since the school had no clearly stated dress code, he should be able to wear whatever he wanted. Mrs. Brody insisted that his clothes were fine for around the house or when he was with friends, but not for the classroom. Should Mrs. Brody be able to tell Andrew what he may or may not wear to her class?

Thoughts and Questions

1. What values is Mrs. Brody trying to teach Andrew?

2. What values is Andrew trying to uphold for himself?

3. Why do we consider one type of clothing appropriate for one occasion and another type for a different situation?

4. Does your school have a dress code? What are its rules? In what ways do you agree or disagree with it?

Characters for Role-playing

1. Andrew

2. Mrs. Brody

3. one of Andrew's parents

4. the principal of the school

5. one of Andrew's friends who likes the way he dresses

Should Rita

Keep Some of

the Change?

Rita's mother sent her to the store to buy some bread, a carton of milk, and a bag of apples. She was instructed to bring home those items as well as a receipt and the exact change.

Rita needed some extra cash, so she was tempted to tell her mother that the items had cost a bit more than she had expected, and that the store clerk had forgotten to hand her a receipt. That way she could keep some of the change. Rita didn't really want to be dishonest, but her allowance was so small compared to what things cost nowadays, and she spent her money very carefully. Her mother would not miss a dollar or so, but the idea bothered Rita. Should she keep some of the change?

Thoughts and Questions

1. Should Rita keep some of the change? What value may she be lacking if she does that?

2. Does it make any difference if Rita's family is rich, poor, or somewhere in between?

3. Does it make any difference what Rita wants to spend the money on?

4. Rita's mother trusts her. Is a dollar or so worth a possible loss of trust? .

5. How might Rita explain to her mother and father why she needs a bigger allowance?

Characters for Role-playing

1. Rita

2. Rita's mother

3. Rita's father

4. Rita's older sister Danielle, who receives a larger allowance than Rita does

How Can Janine Let Her Mother Know That She Must Not Be Kept Home from School to Babysit?

Janine often misses school because her mother asks her to stay home to care for her baby sister. Both of Janine's parents work but they do not make enough money for full-time child care. When their neighbor is not available to care for the baby, Janine is asked to do it. She misses important lessons and tests in school. Janine's mother knows that school is important, but she can't leave a baby alone!

When a teacher asks Janine about her frequent absences, Janine sees a chance to get help. She wonders whether she should ask the teacher to talk to her mother and persuade her to make other arrangements for the baby so that Janine can come to school each day. On the other hand, this might embarrass her mother or make her angry. The baby is important, but so is Janine! What should she do?

Thoughts and Questions

1. What values would our society be demonstrating if we had good, inexpensive child care for all families that needed it?

2. What values are in conflict when Janine's mother realizes that her older child should be in school, but her younger child must have constant care?

3. Is it the business of a school teacher or counselor to talk to Janine's mother about this situation? Why or why not?

4. Do you know a friend or family that has had or has this problem? How was/is it handled? What do *you* think might be a solution?

Characters for Role-playing

1. Janine
2. Janine's mother
3. Janine's teacher or counselor
4. Janine's father

Should Janice Stay Home
in Case Her Grandmother
Needs Her?

Janice is often asked to stay home in the evening when her parents go out or work late. Her elderly grandmother lives with the family and might need Janice's help. Janice is glad to help, but wants to have time with her friends, too. She loves her grandmother but doesn't want to feel so "tied down."

One evening when Janice and her grandmother are home alone, Janice gets a phone call inviting her to a party just down the block. Her grandmother assures her that she can go. Her grandmother says she'll just watch television and go to bed. Janice knows that her parents would not like her to leave the house. What should she do?

Thoughts and Questions

1. How does Janice's family show its values by having the grandmother live with the family?

2. What can be nice about having three generations in one household? What can be annoying about the same situation?

3. What things might have you decide that Janice should stay home? That she should go to the party?

4. How can Janice explain to her parents that she needs more time to be with her friends?

Characters for Role-playing

1. Janice
2. Janice's grandmother
3. Janice's mother
4. Janice's father

Should Martin Say Anything to His Father About His Cheating on His Income Tax Return?

Martin has listened to many talks about honesty from his father. Never cheat on tests in school! Never miss a single house on your newspaper route! If you borrow money from a friend, pay it back as soon as you can! Never take what does not belong to you!

One evening Martin hears his father brag to his mother about the ways he has found to cheat on this year's income tax form! Martin isn't sure what that all includes—something about money his father is pretending was part of his business expenses, and some income he is not reporting. But he clearly heard his father say he was cheating!

After all the talks Martin has heard from his father about honesty, should he say anything to his father? If so, what should he say?

Thoughts and Questions

1. Honesty is an important value. Does Martin's father "practice what he preaches"?

2. Does Martin's father's dishonesty matter so much? After all, the government has plenty of money and will hardly miss the little bit it loses through this man's cheating!

3. Will Martin learn more from his father's words or his father's actions?

4. Would you say anything to the father if you were in Martin's position? What would you say?

Characters for Role-playing

1. Martin
2. Martin's father
3. Martin's mother

Should Tanya Let
Skip Drive
Her Home?

Tanya was psyched to be going to Randi's holiday party. Most of her classmates and some kids from a neighboring school were going to be there. Just as she was putting on a touch of lipstick, she heard her father slam the door to the garage.

"The car's tire is flat and the spare isn't inflated," he groaned. "Skip will have to take you to the party in the truck. And he'll pick you up at 10:00 sharp."

"You owe me big time," quipped Tanya's 17-year-old brother Skip, as she hopped out of his jalopy.

It was close to 11:00 when Skip came to pick up Tanya. He leaned on the horn and waited for her to come outside. When she got into the truck, Tanya smelled beer and noticed empty beer cans on the floor. Skip was drunk. Tanya knew she should never drive with someone who is under the influence of alcohol or drugs, but this was her own brother, and she felt she owed him big time for driving her to the party.

Thoughts and Questions

1. What important values is Skip lacking? How can the lack of these values affect his sister?

2. What difficult choice does Tanya's have to make? Why is she confused about what to do? How might her decision affect her brother's and her own well-being?

3. Have you ever been in a situation similar to Tanya's? If you were, what would you have done? Why?

4. Is there an organization in your area called SADD (Students Against Drunk Driving) that works toward preventing situations such as Tanya's? How might you start a local chapter?

Characters for Role-playing

1. Tanya
2. Skip
3. Tanya and Skip's mother
4. Tanya and Skip's father
5. Randi's parents

Should Kim

Leave the

Store?

Kim, a junior high school student, works in his parents' business, a small grocery store. The whole family works long hours in the store. Even Kim's eight-year-old sister helps out. One afternoon Kim's parents are gone from the store for several hours to pick up some supplies, and Kim is in charge. He is angry that the store takes up nearly all of his after-school hours. He decides to take a short break to go down the street to a music store to see if they have a new tape he wants. He'll only be gone about twenty minutes.

His little sister will stay in the store. She knows how to sell items to customers. Kim will be back before his parents return.

Should Kim go? His parents have told him never to leave his sister alone, especially since the store has been robbed twice. What should he do?

Thoughts and Questions

1. What arguments support Kim's trip to the music store?

2. What points can you make against Kim's trip to the music store?

3. How can Kim convince his parents that he needs more time to himself—to relax, to see friends, to play, to do his school work?

4. Do Kim's parents intend to be mean by keeping him in the store for so many hours? Are there other reasons, needs, and values involved?

5. What values are shown when a whole family like this works hard to make a business succeed?

Characters for Role-playing

1. Kim

2. Kim's little sister

3. Kim's father

4. Kim's mother

How Can Ray Protect Himself from Being Beaten by His Father?

Ray has been coming to school lately with black and blue marks on his arms. When friends ask him what happened, he says, "I bumped into a door" or "I fell off my bike." Finally, the pain is too great. Ray shows a large bruise on his back to his friend Dominic and tells him that his father has been beating him.

Dominic urges Ray to tell a teacher or a counselor so that Ray can be protected. This frightens Ray. What if the school reports his father to the police? His father will be angry and beat him more often! What if they want to send him to a foster home? Frightening thoughts run through Ray's mind.

What should he do?

Thoughts and Questions

1. In many states teachers and all other adults in schools are required by law to report any suspected child abuse to the police. What values do these laws support? Do you agree with these laws?

2. Ray probably has mixed feelings about his father. He probably hates him and loves him at the same time. How can you explain this?

3. Should Ray show his injuries to a teacher or counselor? Should Dominic tell an adult at school what is happening to Ray if Ray will not do it?

4. Have you known anyone who has been treated this harshly by his or her parents? How did you react? Did the person get help?

Characters for Role-playing

1. Ray
2. Dominic
3. a school counselor
4. a police officer
5. Ray's father

Should Debbie

Accept the

Lunch Tickets?

Debbie is often tired in class and finds it hard to pay attention to the lesson. When her teacher asks her about it, she admits that her family has very little money and cannot afford to give her money for lunch. The teacher reminds Debbie that the school has a free lunch program and gives her the paper her parents must fill out. Debbie is embarrassed and knows that her father will yell things about "not taking charity." Debbie has also seen students making fun of those who have the tickets.

The teacher points out that there is nothing dishonorable about accepting the tickets and that Debbie should take advantage of an important program. She offers to speak to Debbie's parents if that will help.

What should Debbie do?

Thoughts and Questions

1. What values are shown by the school and government that provide food for students who cannot afford it?

2. What good values will the teacher be showing if she helps Debbie with this problem? Or is it her business?

3. How might Debbie's father be convinced to accept needed help?

4. Have you seen students make fun of others who participate in such programs? What values are they lacking?

Characters for Role-playing

1. Debbie

2. the teacher who wants to help her

3. Debbie's father

4. the school cafeteria worker in charge of the lunch program

How Can Bob Tell His Father
Not to "Use" Him
Against His Mother?

Bob's parents are divorced. He lives with his mother during the week and usually stays with his father on weekends. Lately his father has been asking him questions about his mother. He wants to know how she spends her money, if she is dating anyone, and what time she gets home at night. Bob is surprised. Up to that time he felt his parents had been dealing with each other and with him in a friendly way. Now his father is asking him to be a spy!

How can Bob tell his father that he must deal with his former wife directly and not make Bob a "go-between" or a spy?

Thoughts and Questions

1. Why might Bob's father be asking Bob these questions?

2. What important matters must parents deal with in relation to their children if they decide to divorce?

3. What are some things Bob could say to his father to see if he can avoid "using" Bob as described above?

4. How many of your friends have divorced parents? What problems—problems like Bob's or any others you know about—do they have to deal with because their parents are no longer together?

5. Should parents always stay together "for the sake of the children," or is divorce sometimes necessary?

Characters for Role-playing

1. Bob
2. Bob's father
3. Bob's mother
4. a friend of Bob's with whom he discusses the problem

Is It Important to Call Your Parents When You Are Going to Be Out Late at Night?

Ernest listened to his parents yelling at his older brother, Eugene. "How many times have we told you to phone us when you are going to be home later than you expected?" their father yelled.

"Don't you know that we worry and need to know where you are and that you are safe?" his mother added.

Eugene replied that at 16 he was old enough to be out with friends without reporting home every minute, that he was careful, and that his parents clearly did not trust him.

Both parents calmed down and explained that when any people live in the same household, regardless of age, all members have a right to know where the others are in case of emergency, and each has a right to know that the others are safe. Surely Eugene would not be comfortable if his parents went out, said they'd be home by 10:00 P.M., and did not show up until many hours later. Wouldn't he wonder if something had happened to them?

Thoughts and Questions

1. What values are Eugene's parents trying to teach him?

2. Eugene wants to be independent and he wants to be trusted. Those are good values. Can he call home when his parents want him to and still achieve both goals?

3. What are your parents' rules concerning when you have to be in and when you have to call them? Do you think their rules are fair for you at your age?

4. Have you ever had to wait for a member of your family to come home far later than you had expected him or her? How did it make you feel?

Characters for Role-playing

1. Eugene
2. Eugene's mother
3. Eugene's father
4. Ernest

How Can Myra Get Her Parents to Understand That Top Grades Are Good Enough?

Myra is one of the best students in her school. She gets "A's" in all of her classes. She takes the hardest math and science classes that many other good students are afraid to try. She is in the honor society and is respected by all her teachers and friends as a terrific student.

Her parents are another story! If she comes home and says, "I got an 'A' on the big math test," her father will say, "Was it the highest 'A' in the class?" If she wants to go out with her friends, even during the day on the weekend, her mother will ask her many times, "Have you done all your homework?" Her mother must know she has! The teachers all say so and she gets all "A's"!

How can she get her parents to see that she is doing very well and they need not worry about her grades in school?

Thoughts and Questions

1. What values is Myra showing by being such a good student?

2. What values are shown by her parents and their questioning? How can they be helped to see that they are pushing too hard?

3. If Myra's parents keep pushing unreasonably, Myra might rebel or feel too much stress. Have any of your friends gone through such experiences? Have you?

4. If you were a friend of Myra's, you might want to tell her that good grades are fine, but friends and a social life are important too. How could you do that in a nice way?

Characters for Role-playing

1. Myra

2. Myra's mother

3. Myra's father

4. Brenda, a friend who invites Myra to a party

Should Rose Tell About the Liquor and Drugs She Saw at the Party?

Rose goes to a party with friends from her eighth-grade class. She has promised her parents that the host's parents would be there and that there would be no liquor or drugs at the party. The host, a very nice boy in her class, had assured her that these things were true.

At the party, Rose discovered that her friend's parents were home, but in a distant part of the house where they could not see what the kids were doing. She also saw beer and marijuana available in the room where the party was going on. She did not know if her friend had lied, or if someone else had brought these to the party. Luckily, when she was invited to try them, she was not pressured when she said, "No, thanks."

Should Rose tell her parents what she saw available at the party?
Should she tell the host's parents?
Should she ignore what she saw?

Thoughts and Questions

1. Why is it so easy for students to have strong values against using drugs or alcohol, but then use them because their friends do?

2. Does it matter that the beer and marijuana were there? After all, no one at the party is old enough to drive, so no accidents will be caused by these substances.

3. What does Rose risk with her friends if she tells her parents or the host's parents?

4. What would you do if you were Rose?

Characters for Role-playing

1. Rose
2. Don, the host of the party
3. Rose's friend, Darcy
4. one of Rose's parents

Should a White Girl Accept a Date with an African American Boy When Her Parents Have Forbidden It?

Elisa's family is white. They have forbidden her ever to accept any invitation or date from a young man who is African American. For a long time Elisa didn't think about it much. She went to a school with students of many races and got along well with people from all groups. At fourteen she didn't think her parents would let her date anyone at all yet, so what they had forbidden had not had much meaning.

One day at school a nice boy named Mal asked her if she'd like to see a movie with him over the weekend. Mal was a boy Elisa had spoken to often in several of her classes and she thought he was very nice and intelligent. Mal was African American. Should she tell her parents about the invitation? Or should she just walk out of the house, tell her mother she is meeting a girlfriend to go shopping, and meet Mal at the movie?

Thoughts and Questions

1. What values do people lack when they will not be with people of races other than their own? What wonderful things do they miss?

2. What might happen if Elisa took Mal to her parents and let them see what a nice young man he is?

3. If Elisa sneaks out of the house to meet Mal, what series of problems might she be starting for herself? In a way, might she not be insulting Mal?

4. Do you have friends of many races? What attitude would you and your parents have toward your dating a person of a race other than your own? Why is it an important topic to think about?

Characters for Role-playing

1. Elisa
2. Mal
3. Elisa's mother
4. Elisa's father

Should Grace Tell Anyone That She Thinks She Is Pregnant?

Grace tells her friend Josie that she thinks she is pregnant. She begs Josie not to tell anyone. She is embarrassed and frightened, but she knows that she should see a doctor. She does not know if she can do that without her parents' permission. She is only fourteen. She knows that if she is really pregnant, she won't be able to hide the problem in a few months.

Grace asks Josie to keep the secret, at least for a while. Josie urges Grace to tell her mother, or another relative, or a school counselor, or the school nurse right away. If she is pregnant, she and her baby should have good care right from the beginning. There is plenty of help in the school system and in the community.

What should Grace do? What should Josie do?

Thoughts and Questions

1. What values will Grace demonstrate if she asks for help right away?

2. What problems might Grace have if she does not ask for help?

3. Josie is a good friend. Should she tell someone if Grace does not?

4. Our society has too many teenage pregnancies; too many children are raised by young women who are really still children themselves. What do you think would be the best way to deal with this problem?

Characters for Role-playing

1. Grace
2. Josie
3. a school counselor or nurse
4. Grace's mother

How Can Lisa Be Shown That Not Everything That Happens to Her Is a Result of Racial Prejudice?

Lisa, a black girl, accuses everyone of prejudice when something goes wrong. If she gets a low grade, the teacher is prejudiced. If she isn't chosen to be a cheerleader, the coach is prejudiced. If another student doesn't talk to her, he or she is prejudiced. If a clerk in a store is rude, he or she is prejudiced against Lisa's race!

Lisa's friends—black, white, and Latino—are getting tired of hearing Lisa say this all the time. Of course, there are still too many prejudiced people around, and sometimes Lisa is correct. But most of the time she is wrong, and her friends recognize it. They want to talk to her to try to help her improve her attitude. She is too angry at too many people and she is denying herself the chance to get to know quite a few nice people!

Thoughts and Questions

1. Of course, many people still have racial, religious, and other prejudices. What values do they lack?

2. How might Lisa's friends bring up the topic with her so they can all discuss it in a calm way?

3. What are some real examples of prejudices you have seen in your own life?

4. Have you ever made the mistake Lisa often makes—thinking you had seen prejudice that actually was not there? Tell what happened.

Characters for Role-playing

1. Lisa

2. Rosa, another black girl

3. Elvia, a Latina

4. Terry, a white boy

Tough Decisions

How Can Antonia Combat the Hurtful Questions?

Antonia is a new girl in school, an immigrant from Bulgaria. She speaks English well, has a friendly manner, and is well accepted. Some students ask her well-meaning but hurtful questions. They do not always choose their words well. How come you know English so well? Are you a legal alien? Do they eat funny food in your country? When are you going to get a more up-to-date haircut?

After one question, Antonia screams, "Leave me alone!" Her friends are shocked because they did not think they had been rude.

How can Antonia explain to her friends how she feels?

Thoughts and Questions

1. What good values are the other girls showing by wanting to know about Antonia and her background?

2. What are some ways the girls could word their questions so they would not seem rude or hurtful? Are there some questions they should leave out entirely?

3. What values did Antonia's family show by moving to the United States? What do you think are the reasons they wanted to come here?

4. How many immigrant students are in your school? Do they seem to have any problems getting used to a new school, language, and country? How might you help them?

Characters for Role-playing

1. Antonia
2. Sonia, an immigrant from Belarus
3. Sean, an American-born boy
4. Sarah, an American-born girl

How Can Amanda Combat Prejudice Against Her Because Her Family Is Wealthy?

Amanda comes from a wealthy home. Her parents are both lawyers and own the biggest house in the neighborhood. Amanda wears expensive clothes and has told her friends about her family's vacations in Europe.

Some girls have accused Amanda of being snobby and standoffish. In fact, she is nothing like that at all. Her parents have purposely sent her to the local public school instead of the expensive private school they can afford. Amanda does not brag about her family's money and does not like being stereotyped. Her close friends appreciate her true personality, but others need convincing.

Should Amanda try to say anything to those who see her as a "rich snob," or should she ignore such nonsense?

Thoughts and Questions

1. Should Amanda say anything to the girls who say she's a snob, or should she just continue to be herself and hope they will see her true, friendly ways?

2. Amanda wears expensive clothes and mentions European vacations. Does that automatically make her a snob?

3. What values do Amanda's parents probably consider important if they send her to public school?

4. Have you ever thought rich people you met were snobs who keep their distance from those with less money? Did you turn out to be right or wrong?

5. What values might a person lack if he or she judges others based on how much money they have?

Characters for Role-playing

1. Amanda

2. Jill, Amanda's best friend

3. Toni, a girl who thinks Amanda is a snob

4. Anne, a girl who has just met Amanda for the first time

How Can Tom's Friends Keep Him from Running Away?

Tom lives with his mother and stepfather. Tom's stepfather is very strict and Tom does not like him. Tom has talked about running away from home. His friends get scared when they hear him talk like that.

Some of his friends try to get Tom to see if he can stay at his best friend's house for a while, and also have some serious talks with his stepfather about how they could get along better. Tom is very stubborn. His friends are afraid that he might really run away and live in the streets if he had to!

What are some good ways Tom could get help?

What are some things his friends should advise him to do?

Thoughts and Questions

1. Why might it be a good idea for Tom to stay with his best friend for a while if both his family and the friend's family allow it?

2. What values will the friend's family be showing when they allow Tom to stay with them?

3. What values will Tom's stepfather be showing if he has serious talks with Tom about how the two of them can get along better?

4. Have you ever had a friend who had Tom's difficult situation? What happened?

Characters for Role-playing

1. Tom
2. Tom's stepfather
3. Tom's mother
4. Tom's best friend, Rudy
5. Rudy's mother

How Can Marina Help
Her Neighbor's
Mistreated Animals?

Marina loves animals and plans to become a veterinarian. She was delighted last year when her neighbor, Mr. Bauer, asked her to help care for his pets—three horses, eleven cats, three dogs, one pig, one iguana. Marina jumped at the chance, and she faithfully fed and groomed the animals every day.

About two months ago, the neighbor told Marina that she was no longer needed. When Marina delivered Girl Scout cookies to the neighbor, she couldn't help but notice how mangy and thin the animals looked. There was no clean hay in the horses' stalls and the pig pen was filthy. Marina suspected the animals were being mistreated and that this was a case of animal cruelty.

What can Marina do to help these animals and to educate others about the serious offense of cruelty to animals?

Thoughts and Questions

1. What values are people lacking when they mistreat animals? Do you think it is a crime to mistreat animals?

2. What values does Marina have for caring about the treatment of animals? How might she help her neighbor and the animals?

3. How can Marina encourage her friends to get involved with an organization that helps prevent cruelty to animals?

4. Are there any books, films, or speakers that could inform the class about animal cruelty or neglect?

Characters for Role-playing

1. Marina
2. Mr. Bauer
3. Norma and Tyler, Marina's friends
4. Mr. Jackson, Marina's teacher
5. A guest speaker from the ASPCA

How Can Margaret Deal with Her Weight Problem?

Margaret is overweight. Some of the other students make fun of her appearance, especially when she wears big "tent" dresses to hide her weight.

Margaret's friends appreciate her friendly personality and sense of humor, but mean comments from other students hurt Margaret a great deal. Lately, she's become so unhappy that she's stopped eating. She skips lunch, and at the local hangout, she orders water when her friends order sodas. Margaret's friends read an article about a singer obsessed with being thin who died from not eating. They're worried about Margaret.

How can Margaret and her friends stop others from making nasty comments about Margaret's weight? Is there any way they could help Margaret lose weight sensibly?

Thoughts and Questions

1. What values are people lacking when they judge others by such things as weight and appearance?

2. What can Margaret's friends do to support her efforts to lose weight so that she will feel better about herself and improve her health?

3. How does our society exaggerate the need to be very thin? Do you see any proof of this in advertising you have seen?

4. How have you noticed heavy people being treated or talked about? Have you ever tried to ask people to make kind rather than mean comments?

Characters for Role-playing

1. Margaret
2. Charisse, Margaret's good friend
3. Noah, a boy who makes fun of Margaret
4. the school nurse

Should the Party Date Be Changed for Joshua?

Joshua is Jewish and comes from an observant, religious family. When his school's graduation party at the local amusement park is planned for a Friday night, the beginning of the Jewish Sabbath, he knows he cannot attend. He makes no complaint—he did not expect a class activity to be planned around him! There are other Jewish students in the school, but they are not as religious as Joshua is and they will attend the party.

Although Joshua does not complain, another student mentions the problem in a student council meeting. She suggests that the party could be on a Thursday night so that Joshua and any other student with his beliefs would be able to attend. What should the student council decide? There is still time to change the date of the party.

Thoughts and Questions

1. What values are clearly important to Joshua if he does not go to the class party?

2. What values are being shown by the girl who brings up the topic at the student council meeting?

3. Since Joshua himself did not complain, what is the point of considering a change at all?

4. How would you vote if you were on the student council? Explain your decision.

Characters for Role-playing

1. Joshua

2. Joyce, the girl who suggested that the council change the date of the party

3. the teacher who is in charge of the party plans

4. one of Joshua's parents

Notes

Notes